ArchiScapes

Color Your Imagination Wild!

MindWare.
brainy toys for kids of all ages.

w w w . m i n d w a r e . c o m

MindWare Original Coloring Books

From ancient art to optical illusions, our unique coloring books feature intricate details and dazzling patterns, providing hours of imaginative fun. Our artist-quality markers and colored pencils are the perfect companions. Visit www.mindware.com to see our full selection.

40096 **24 Markers**

52150 **18 Colored Pencils**

25075 **Hidden Fur**

80185 **PrismDesigns**

40010 **Optical Art Illuminations**

36020 **Hidden Transformations**

48150 **Color Counts: Animals**

91007 **EnviroScapes**

36017 **Modern Patterns Illusions**

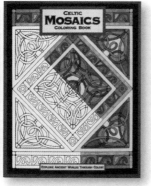

15003 **Celtic Mosaic**

95120 **EcoLights**

ISBN 978-1-892069-19-1
SKU 91005

for other MindWare products visit
www.mindware.com

2/2012

ArchiScapes

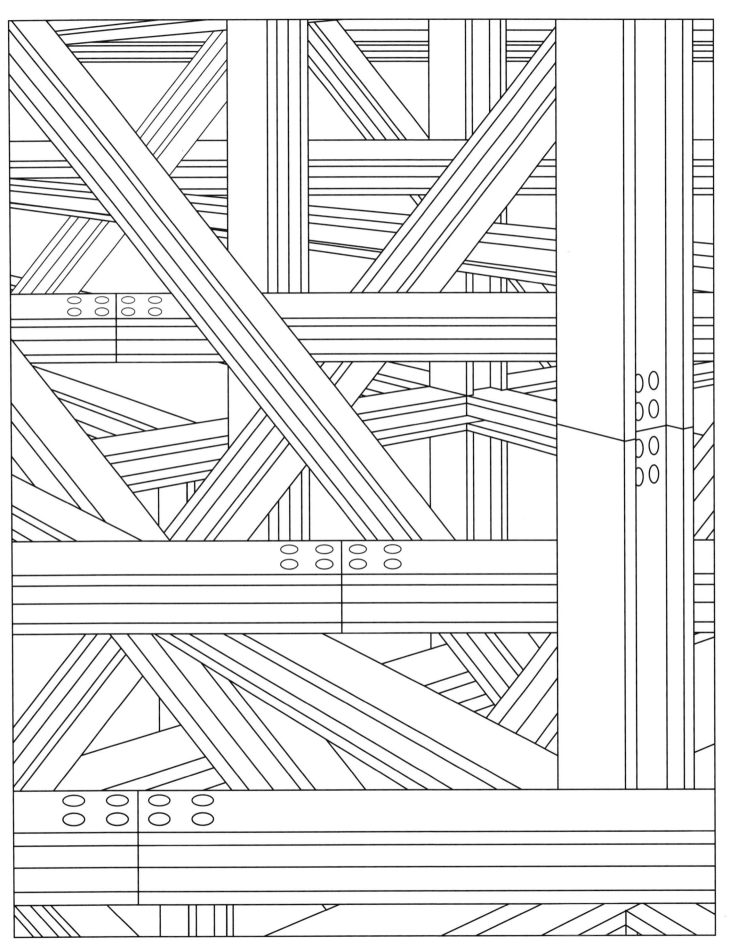

ArchiScapes

ArchiScapes

ArchiScapes

ArchiScapes

ArchiScapes

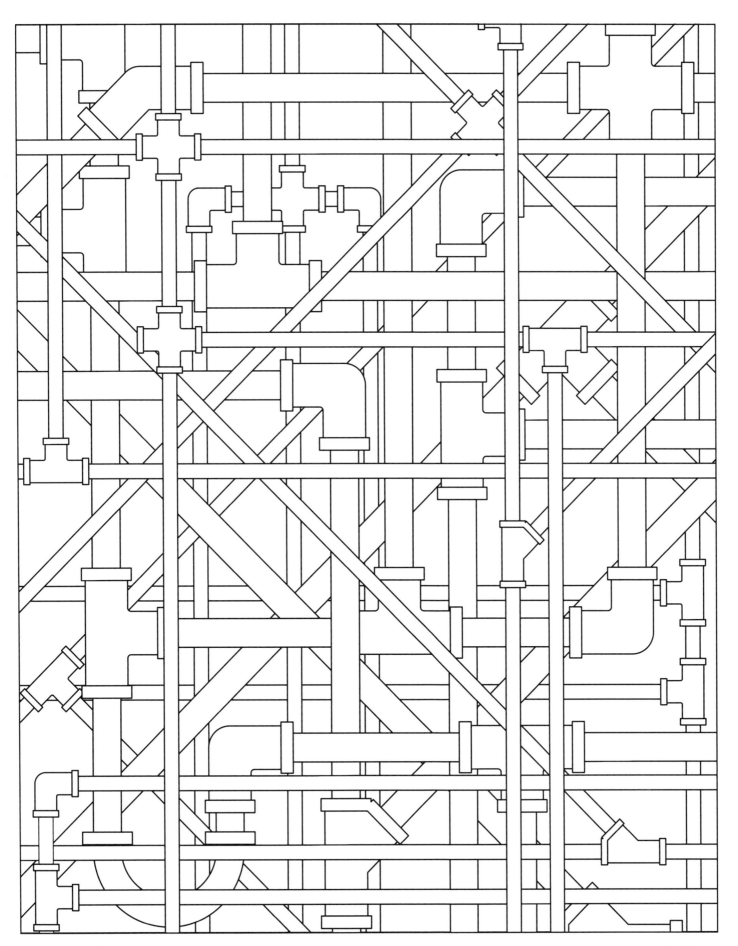

ArchiScapes

ArchiScapes

ArchiScapes

ArchiScapes

ArchiScapes

ArchiScapes

ArchiScapes

ArchiScapes

ArchiScapes

ArchiScapes

ArchiScapes

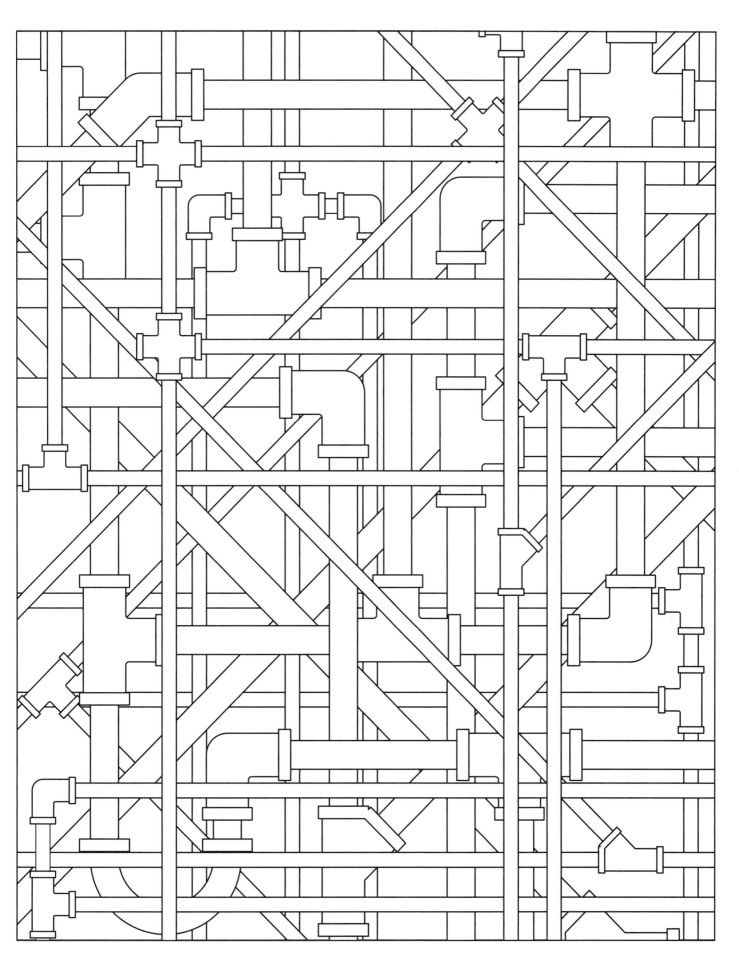

ArchiScapes

ArchiScapes

ArchiScapes

ArchiScapes

ArchiScapes

ArchiScapes